CHLOÉ CRUCHAUDET
DESERTER'S
MASQUERAD

BASED ON LA GARÇONNE ET L'ASS
BY FABRICE VIRGILI AND DANIÈLE VOL

KNOCKABOUT

Deserter's Masquerade by Chloé Cruchaudet
© Editions Delcourt - 2013.

Based on the essay La Garçonne et l'Assassin by
Fabrice Virgili and Danièle Voldman
© Editions Payot & Rivages - 2010.

Translated from the French by Frank Wynne.

This English language edition published by
Knockabout Limited
42 c Lancaster Road London W11 1QR
United Kingdom.

Back cover photo of Paul Grappe, alias Suzanne,
from the Paris National Archive, taken by
Maurice Garçon.

A CIP catalogue record for this book is available
from the British Library.

Print edition ISBN 9780861662586

Digital edition ISBN 9780861662598

www.knockabout.com

Printed in China

First printing April 2017

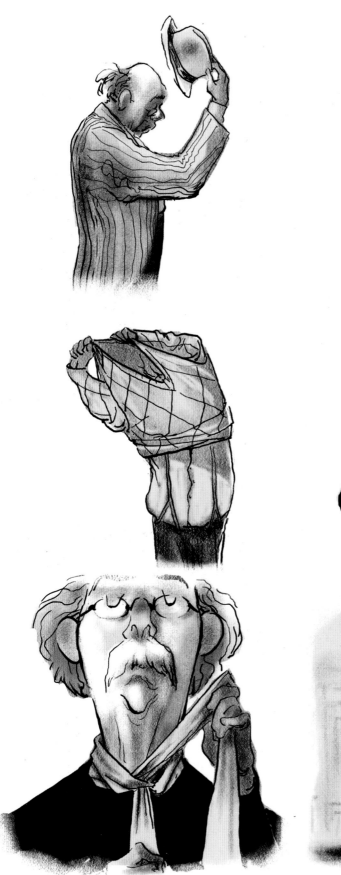

4

i JUST WANT YOU TO BE SENSIBLE.

...DON'T BE LIKE ME...

CHOOSE A GOOD MAN, SOMEONE RELIABLE, SOMEONE YOU CAN DEPEND ON...

MAMAN...

...i'M JUST GOING DANCING TO HAVE A LITTLE FUN, DON'T MAKE SUCH A FUSS...

ALRIGHT, ALRIGHT... SIT UP STRAIGHT, YOU LOOK LIKE A SACK OF POTATOES.

AND DON'T FORGET TO LOWER YOUR EYES WHEN A GENTLEMAN LOOKS AT YOU, YOU DON'T WANT TO SEEM BRAZEN.

YOU SURE YOU'D DON'T WANT TO WAIT AND HAVE A LITTLE SOUP?

I'D BETTER GO - MY CLOTHES ALREADY SMELL OF LEEKS.

YOU'RE A HANDSOME LAD, SON. YOU'LL HAVE THE GIRLS FLOCKING AROUND YOU.

I LIKE THAT JACKET. GIVES YOU NICE BROAD SHOULDERS.

GO ON, YOU RASCAL.

TARNATION... NOT BEFORE TIME...

LISTEN, ME AND GINO WERE TALKING...

...YOU'VE BEEN BORING US BOTH TO TEARS ABOUT THIS TART OF YOURS.

TONIGHT HAS TO BE THE BIG NIGHT.

YOU NEED TO GET IN THERE!

OOOOOH... LOUISE...

GIVE IT A REST, WILL YOU?

MWA MWA MWAAAA.

LISTEN UP. IF YOU WANT TO SEDUCE HER, JUST KEEP TALKING, FLATTER HER, SWEET-TALK HER TALK, ANYTHING — IT WORKS.

NO. SHE'S TOO SMART, SHE'S NOT GOING TO FALL FOR ANY OLD FLANNEL.

I THINK I'LL PLAY THE MYSTERIOUS LONE WOLF...

FLASH HER MY CRYPTIC "LOOK" — THAT ALWAYS GETS GIRLS WET.

YOUR WHAT LOOK?

ENIGMATIC...

YOU SAY NOTHING, YOU STARE... THEN BOW YOUR HEAD AND FLASH HER A ROGUISH LOOK AND A MISCHIEVOUS SMILE...

DON'T, THAT'S SCARY.

10

11

HE'S NO TOFF, HE'S NO SWELL
HE'S A REAL MAAAAN.

15

19

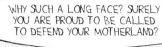

You're a fine soldier, strong as an ox! You'll have the Boche on their knees!

Right lads... let's go give the Hun a swift kicking - with a bit of luck by the autumn we'll be back in Paris to sample the new wine.

25

26

I'M SO SORRY, MARCEL...

THE TRIP TO THE DANCE HALL...
THE BOTTLES OF WINE...
I'LL DRINK ONE FOR YOU,
YOU'LL BE WITH ME IN SPIRIT...

BUT... WHO'S SAYS YOU'LL GET OUT ALIVE?
YOU'LL DIE LIKE A BRAVE LITTLE SOLDIER.
YOUR LOUISE WILL MAKE A LOVELY WIDOW...
WHAT A FUTURE !

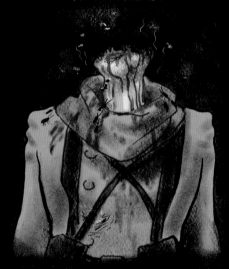

SO...
YOU THINK MAYBE THIS
MIGHT BE THE MOMENT TO PROVE
THAT YOU'RE A REAL MAN?

HEAR THAT? THE BELLS...
IT'S THE STRETCHER BEARERS...

32

PSST!

IF YOU FANCIED GIVING ME YOUR RATION OF PLONK...

... I COULD GIVE YOU SOME INFECTED PUS. INTERESTED?

I'M KEEPING THE PLONK, BUT I COULD GIVE YOU MY BISCUITS FOR A WEEK...

DEAL.

SO... IT DOESN'T SEEM TO WANT TO HEAL, THIS NASTY LITTLE INFECTION...

THAT'S VERY UNFORTUNATE. I SHALL NEED A DETAILED REPORT...

KNOCK! KNOCK!

MADAME GRAPPE! IT'S ME...

WHERE IS HE?

HE'S WAITING AT THE END OF THE HANGAR.

GET HIM OUT. IT'S TOO DANGEROUS. THE GENDARMES ARE BOUND TO SEARCH THE PLACE SOONER OR LATER.

PAUL?

PSST...

ARE YOU SICK IN THE HEAD? WHY DID YOU DO IT?

I BROUGHT YOU SOME DRIED TOMATOES AND SOME PÂTÉ...

OOH... LOUISE...

OOH...

SORRY... BUT I'VE SPENT MONTHS WAITING FOR THIS MOMENT...

DON'T WORRY. OPEN A BOTTLE OF WINE.

38

40

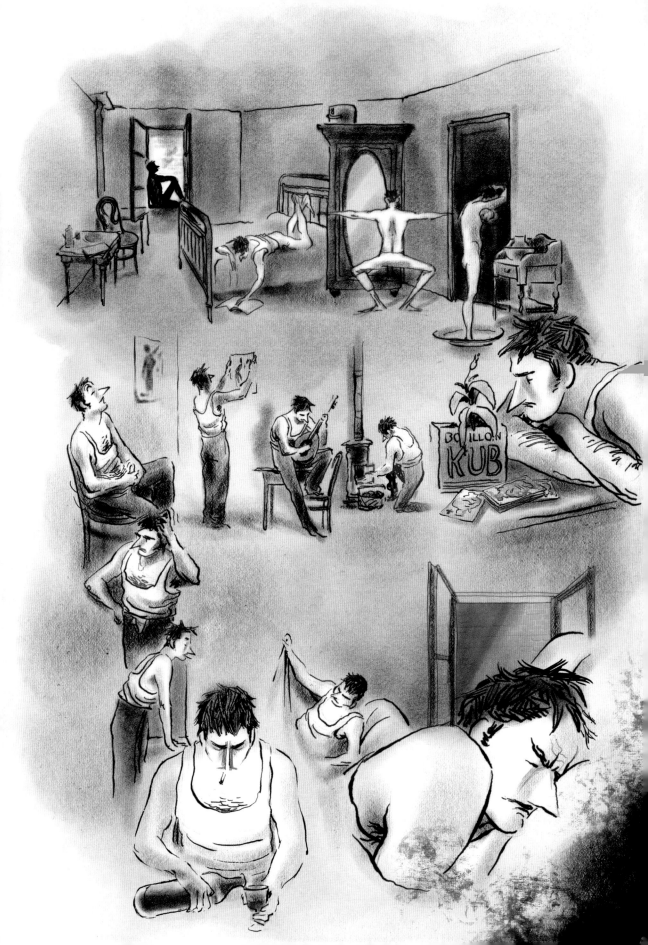

44

46

54

WELL?

NOT BAD... A BIT TIGHT IN THE CHEST, BUT IT'LL DO...

WHAT MATTERS IS THAT I CAN GO OUT, PICK VIOLETS IN THE WOODS, CAN YOU SMELL. THAT? IT'S ALMOST SPRING...

PAUL...

...A DRESS ISN'T ENOUGH.

IN BROAD DAYLIGHT YOU WOULDN'T FOOL ANYONE FOR A SECOND.

WHAT? WHAT ELSE DO I NEED? I JUST SWAY ME HIPS AND VOILÀ.

WHAT ARE YOU TALKING ABOUT? I SHAVED THIS MORNING... I CAN HARDLY SHAVE EVERY TWO HOURS...

WELL... I CAN SEE STUBBLE...

WELL, YOU DO WHAT YOU LIKE, BUT... YOU'RE A FRIGHT. PEOPLE WILL THINK YOU'RE AN INVERT AND YOU'LL GET THROWN IN JAIL...

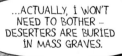

...AND WHEN THEY FIND OUT WHO YOU REALLY ARE, I'LL HAVE TO BUY YOU A PLOT IN PÈRE LACHAISE...

...ACTUALLY, I WON'T NEED TO BOTHER – DESERTERS ARE BURIED IN MASS GRAVES.

ALRIGHT, ALRIGHT, STOP MOCKING ME AND START TELLING ME WHAT TO DO!

YOU'RE MAKING ME NERVOUS NOW... WHAT IS IT?

YOU WANT TO DO THINGS PROPERLY, DON'T YOU?

ER... YEAH...

WELL, FOR THAT I NEED TO GO AN SEE A FRIEND WHO'S BETTER EQUIPPED THAN I AM. SHE MENTIONED SHE'S GOT THE LATEST GADGETS FROM LONDON. THAT SHOULD BE USEFUL.

WHAT GADGETS? WHAT DO YOU MEAN?

SEE YOU SOON, MY PRETTY.

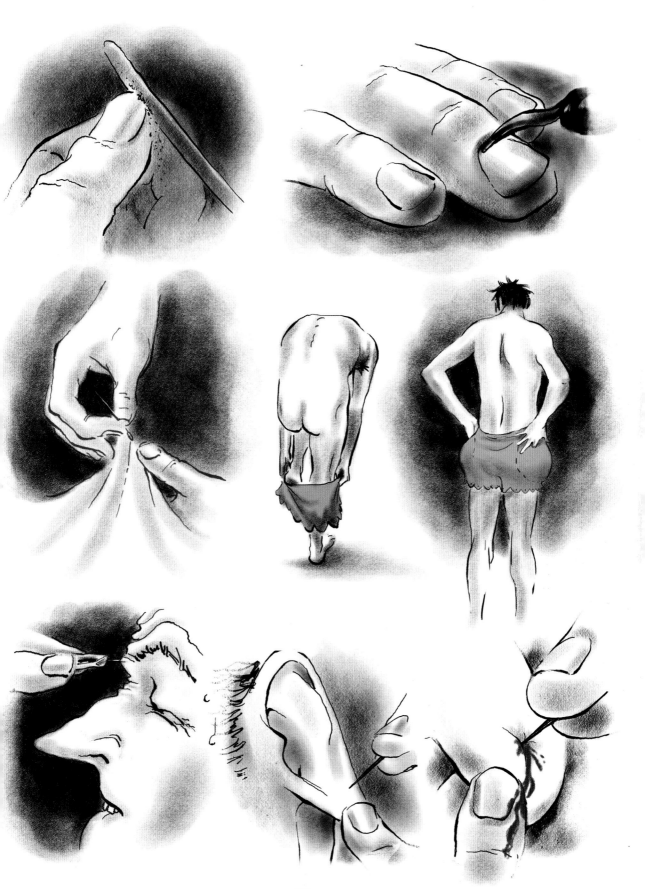

61

* the name of a French aperitif

IF YOU SAY SO... BUT YOU'LL SEE, WITH THE DRESS AND THE ACCESSORIES, THE MOVEMENTS WILL COME NATURALLY.
HERE, TAKE THIS...
AND TRY TO LOOK MANLY WHILE YOU OPEN IT...
MADEMOISELLE!

67

70

I COULDN'T BEAR IT, YOU KNOW...

I MEAN...
SEEING YOU COME HOME LIKE THAT...
TO ME, IT DOESN'T MATTER THAT YOU DIDN'T
DEFEND YOUR COUNTRY TO THE END...

MY COUNTRY?
OH, POOR LITTLE LOUISE,
YOU REALLY DON'T HAVE A CLUE!

IF YOU KNEW HOW
LITTLE I CARE ABOUT
THAT JINGOISTIC CRAP!

SHHH...
NOT SO LOUD...

NO... WHAT REALLY UPSETS ME
IS BEING SUCH A BURDEN TO YOU...
THE TWO OF US ARE LIVING OFF YOUR RATION CARD...
IT CAN'T GO ON...

I MEAN...
IF I HAD STAYED, YOU'D BE A WAR WIDOW
WITH A NICE LITTLE PENSION...

WHAT ARE YOU
SAYING, PAUL?

UGH... IT SMELLS LIKE THE TRENCHES...
EVEN THEIR CLOTHES ARE SODDEN
WITH THE STENCH OF FEAR...

IT TURNS MY STOMACH.
I'LL SEE YOU BACK AT HOME.

73

PAUL, I'VE BEEN THINKING...

...AND YOU'RE RIGHT. WE CAN'T CARRY ON LIKE THIS.

YOU'RE SAT HERE AND WE'RE STARVING TO DEATH.

I KNOW, BUT WHAT AM I SUPPOSED TO DO...?

WHAT'S THIS?

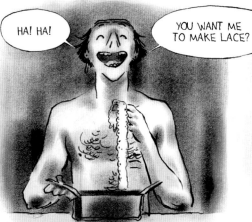

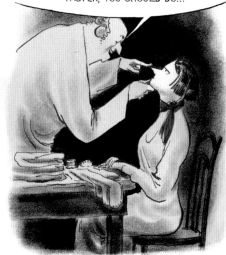

OH MY WORD, THIS FABRIC IS SO LIGHT, SO SHEER... IT WEIGHS NOTHING!

PURE CHIFFON... PRETTY, HUH? IT'S LIKE A BREATH OF WIND...

WE USE IT TO MAKE LITTLE SUMMER BOLEROS.

OH LA LA! IT'S LIKE BEING IN A CLOUD!

SOMETIMES WE EMBROIDER IT AND ADD LACE RUFFS TO MAKE A CORSET.

BUT WHEN IT COMES TO LUXURY, I THINK THERE'S NOTHING LIKE SILK CREPE DE CHINE...

ORGANDIE, CASHMERE, THEY'RE SO LOVELY.

FEEL IT? SOFT AS A PEACH.

BUT... IT'S NOT LIKE WE GET TO WEAR IT – IT'S FOR THE UPPER CLASSES

BACK TO WORK, LADIES, RIGHT NOW!

81

HONEST TO GOD, I REALLY DON'T UNDERSTAND ANYTHING ANYMORE...

... I DIDN'T REALISE THAT THIS SWEATSHOP WAS A DEN OF DYKES!

HUH! MAYBE THEY'RE NOT DYKES...

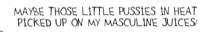

MAYBE THOSE LITTLE PUSSIES IN HEAT PICKED UP ON MY MASCULINE JUICES!

...BUT I CAN'T HELP IT IF THEY'RE ALL CRAZY ABOUT ME!

YEAH...
WELL STOP PAWING THEM ALL THE TIME AND THEY WON'T SMELL YOU...

AAAAH...
AM I DREAMING OR AM I SENSING SOMETHING...

...SOMETHING LIKE JEALOUSY, HMM?

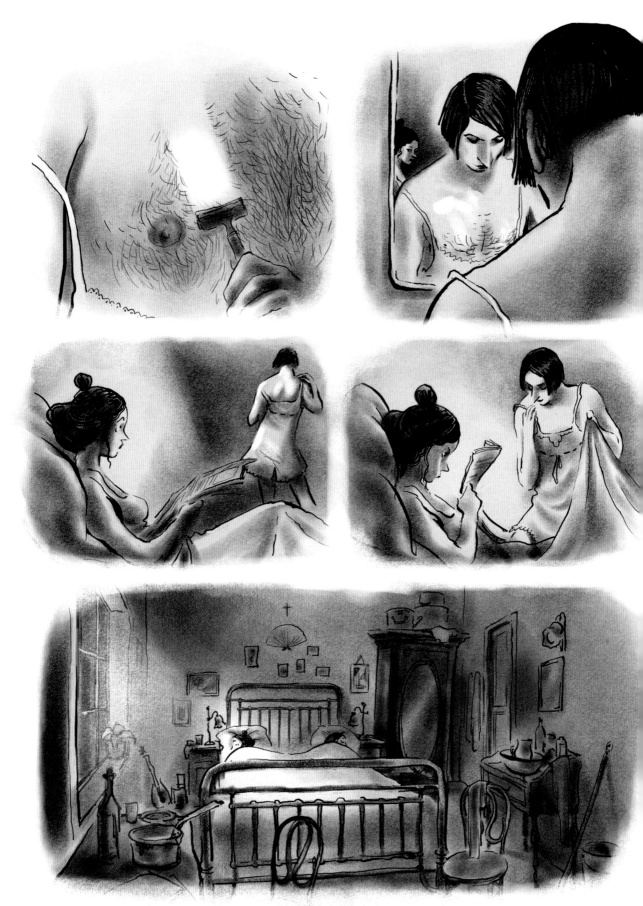

YOU NEED TO WORK A LITTLE HARDER OTHERWISE MONSIEUR WILL NOT BE VERY HAPPY AND SUZANNE MIGHT NOT GET HER POCKET MONEY...

HEE! HEE!

AH, MY LITTLE PET. NOT TOO TIRED FROM ALL THIS GOSSIPING?

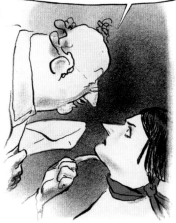

PFFF...

WHY DOES HE TALK TO ME AS THOUGH I'M A MENTAL DEFECTIVE?

HE FANCIES YOU, THAT'S WHY!

WELL, WHAT I FANCY IS SPENDING THIS HAVING FUN IN THE BOIS DE BOULOGNE ON SUNDAY!

WHEN A SUNNY SUNDAY KNELLS PRIGGISH MAIDS AND NE'ER-DO-WELLS PANDERS, CROOKS AND PRETTY BELLES COME SIP A GLASS OF BOURGOGNE DOWN IN THE BOIS DE BOULOGNE.

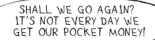

86

93

LOUISE IS SUCH A STUPID GIRL...

OF COURSE WE NOTICED WHAT A VIRILE HE-MAN YOU WERE STRAIGHT AWAY...

WHERE IS SUZANNE?

I'VE NO IDEA. SHE DIDN'T WANT TO LEAVE WITH US. NOW LET ME WORK.

IN ANY CASE, GIVEN THE STATE SHE WAS IN LAST NIGHT, SHE WOULDN'T BE ABLE TO HOLD A NEEDLE.

INTERESTING.

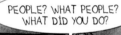

99

WHY ON EARTH PAY MONEY FOR THOSE?

I DIDN'T PAY MONEY FOR ANYTHING — THEY'RE GOING TO PAY ME. YOU'RE ALWAYS ACCUSING ME OF WASTING MONEY, SO I GOT A JOB.

IT'S PRETTY SIMPLE. THEY GAVE ME THE FIGURINES, THE POTS OF PAINT...

...IT JUST NEEDS A CAREFUL, DELICATE HAND. IT SHOULD SUIT ME.

YEAH... WITH THE SLAP YOU PAINT ON EVERY MORNING, YOU'VE HAD LOTS OF PRACTICE...

HA! HA! VERY FUNNY...

104

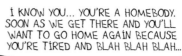

HERE SHE IS!

HERE'S THE QUEEN!

HI, SUZY!

WHO'S THIS?

IT'S THE WIFE.

I'M JUST HERE FOR MY HUSBAND...

RIGHT... WE'LL TAKE A LITTLE STROLL, GET OURSELVES WARMED UP. WE'LL SEE YOU LATER.

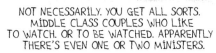

111

112

THERE ARE HETEROSEXUALS AND HOMOSEXUALS JUST AS THERE ARE MEN AND THERE ARE WOMEN. ONE IS EITHER ONE OR THE OTHER, THAT IS ALL.

TO GET BACK TO THE POINT. WHAT WAS THE NATURE OF YOUR RELATIONSHIP WITH MONSIEUR GRAPPE?

WELL... WE MET IN THE WOODS. EVERYONE THERE KNEW SUZANNE...

SHE WAS A REAL CHARACTER !

AND... HOW DO YOU EXPLAIN HER... HIS SUCCESS?

OH...

IT'S DIFFICULT TO SAY... SUZANNE WAS A REMARKABLE CREATURE, SHE WAS RADIANT.

SOMETIMES, IF THE WEATHER WAS BAD, THERE WERE NOT MANY PEOPLE IN THE WOODS...

WE WERE THERE FOR THE PLEASURE, TO LIVE OUT OUR FANTASIES... BUT AS WE GOT TO KNOW EACH OTHER, IT BECAME CLEAR THAT SOME WERE IN GREATER FINANCIAL DIFFICULTY THAN OTHERS, AND SO...

...IN A SENSE, IT WAS A KIND OF MUTUAL AID.

COULD YOU TELL THE COURT WHAT TYPE OF PEOPLE MONSIEUR GRAPPE USUALLY FREQUENTED?

OH... SUZANNE LIKED PEOPLE WHO WERE ELEGANT, REFINED, SOPHISTICATED.

AND WERE THERE DRUGS? HEROIN, COCAINE?

FOR THOSE WHO COULD AFFORD THEM. FOR THE OTHERS THERE WAS ALCOHOL, CANNABIS...

MY GOD... THE SHAME...

AND WHAT DID MONSIEUR GRAPPE CONSUME?

ALCOHOL, A LOT OF ALCOHOL, AND A LITTLE OF EVERYTHING ELSE

MAY I REMIND YOU THAT THE COUPLE'S SOLE INCOME WAS THE PITTANCE LOUISE EARNED AS A SEAMSTRESS. SO, EFFECTIVELY MONSIEUR GRAPPE WENT WITH THOSE WHO HAD SOMETHING TO OFFER.

YOUR HONOUR, I THINK YOU WILL AGREE:

PAUL GRAPPE PROSTITUTED HIMSELF AND PIMPED HIS OWN WIFE.

NO, NO! IT WAS MUCH MORE SUBTLE THAN THAT... WE...

HOW WOULD YOU DESCRIBE PAUL'S ATTITUDE TO HIS WIFE?

AT FIRST, I WOULD SAY... INDIFFERENT. IT WAS AS IF SUZANNE WAS EMBARRASSED BY LOUISE. HE WOULD LEAVE HER IN THE ARMS OF A STRANGER WHILE HE AMUSED HIMSELF ELSEWHERE.

BUT AFTER A TIME, IT CHANGED LOUISE... HOW CAN I PUT THIS? SHE ADAPTED TO OUR WORLD AND THAT SEEMED TO INFURIATE SUZANNE. THAT SAID, EVEN IF THEIR RELATIONSHIP SUFFERED, THEY KEPT COMING. YOU QUICKLY BECOME HOOKED ON THE RUSH OF ADRENALIN...

AH! AT LAST!

WHERE THE HELL WERE YOU?

NOT SO LOUD... I'VE GOT A TERRIBLE HANGOVER.

WHAT A NIGHTMARE... I LOOKED EVERYWHERE FOR YOU BEFORE GIVING UP...

...MARCEL TOOK ME HOME. IT WAS LATE. I DIDN'T HAVE MONEY FOR A TAXI... I SLEPT A COUPLE OF HOURS AT HIS. I'M SHATTERED...

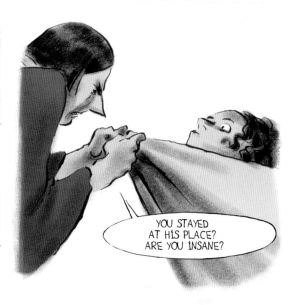

YOU STAYED AT HIS PLACE? ARE YOU INSANE?

120

121

I PICKED UP A NEW BATCH OF FIGURINES. I'M GOING TO TRY AND PAINT THEM ALL TODAY...

SEE YOU.

WELL, THERE YOU GO, THIS WAY THERE'S NO DOUBT I'M A MAN!

SILLY BOY... LOOSEN THOSE BRACES NOW – IT'S OBSCENE!

DAMN...JUST LOOK AT ALL THESE MOTH HOLES.

PFF... WEAR A JACKET, NO ONE WILL NOTICE.

128

131

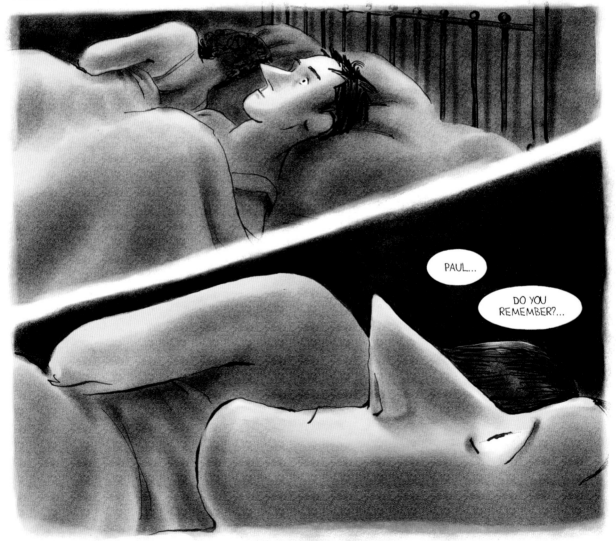

134

135

137

138

139

143

WELL ISN'T THIS IRONIC?

I COME HOME EMPTY-HANDED. I'D JUST MADE A BIG DECISION.

TO GIVE UP THE BOOZE...

...BECAUSE I LOVE YOU.

145

151

153

155

157

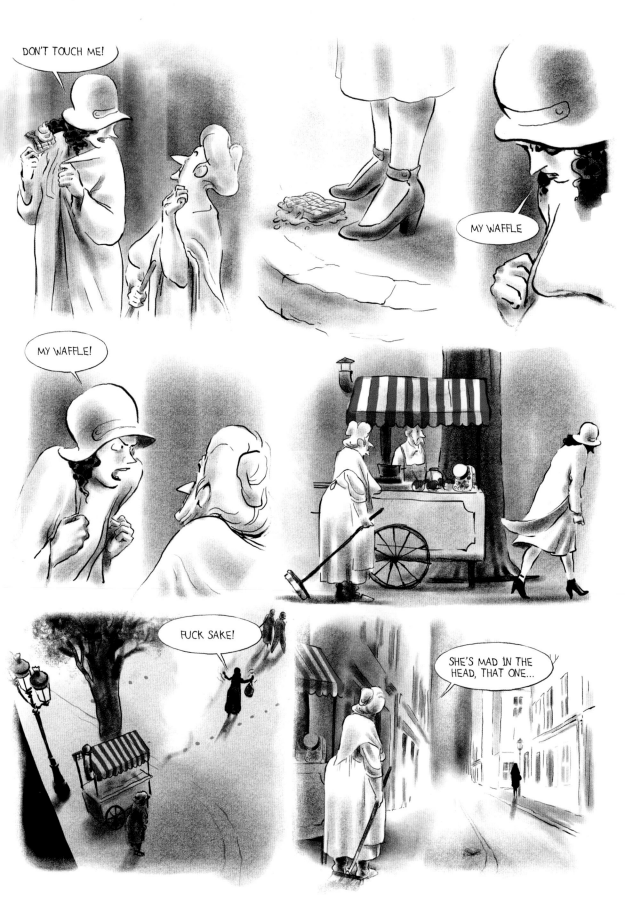

159

160